Dare to Sparkle

30 days of self-care bravery. Be the fearless goddess that you are meant to be and shine bright.

Lou Meggiato

Published by Mandala Essentials

First edition October 2020

Written by Lou Meggiato
Composition by Lou Meggiato & Chris Brennan

ISBN 978-1-7773840-0-5 (paperback)
ISBN 978-1-7773840-1-2 (hardcover)
ISBN 978-1-7773840-2-9 (ebook)

To Adrian—the guy that told me the most valuable advice. Do what makes you happy because that is what you deserve.

To Ezra, Evie and Korbie—for supporting their mama in all that she does and all that she dreams about.

To my mama and papa—for supporting in all I have ever done and always with an open heart.

INTRODUCTION

Hello lovelies! Yes, I am talking to you. You are truly a gift to the world. I know you might be wondering who is this person to tell me this? She doesn't know me. You are right, but often what others see in us is not what we see in ourselves. We cloud our view in judgement and not being enough.

Hey I'm Lou and this book is my gift to you. My hope is that you will not only find your own inner light and sunshine but that you will inspire others to do the same. I'd like to think that this book might help the process. Perhaps you will even be inspired to chase after your own happiness and realize just how amazing you are. That you might be encouraged to create an ongoing self-care practice for yourself and realize that you should be your own priority.

Whatever your beliefs or religion are, please know that we were put on this earth to shine, to sparkle and to inspire. That is a pretty scary thought for most of us. Change is also scary because it's daring to discover the unknowns. This is the first step.

You truly are amazing, beautiful, awesome and it's time to unleash that on the world. Don't play small, period. Don't wrap yourself up in so much busyness that you have no time to spend on you. Your worth is not based on your success or your ability to look after 5 people or being indispensable to your job.

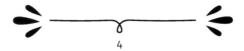

This next piece has truly inspired my whole journey of daring to sparkle. So much so, I even have it tattooed on my arm.

*Our deepest fear is not that we are inadequate.
Our deepest fear is that we are powerful beyond measure. It is our light, not our darkness that most frightens us. We ask ourselves, Who am I to be brilliant, gorgeous, talented, and fabulous? Actually, who are you not to be? You are a child of God. Your playing small does not serve the world. There is nothing enlightened about shrinking so that other people will not feel insecure around you. We are all meant to shine, as children do. We were born to make manifest the glory of God that is within us. It is not just in some of us; it is in everyone and as we let our own light shine, we unconsciously give others permission to do the same. As we are liberated from our own fear, our presence automatically liberates others.*
–Marianne Deborah Williamson

Marianne Deborah Williamson(born 8 July 1952) is a spiritual activist, author, lecturer, and founder of The Peace Alliance, a grass roots campaign supporting legislation currently before Congress to establish a United States Department of Peace.

This workbook is an adventure into you. It is a chance to discover the truth of what lights your soul and brings you joy. It is an opportunity to dig a little deeper into what makes you feel worthy and enough right now.

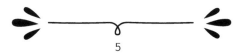

I have been on my own journey of awakening. I have had to find my own inner warrior and inner goddess to get through my life's challenges. In daring to sparkle, I found my passion for helping others to see the light I could see in them, but they couldn't yet.

I have led women for years through sharing the nurturing tools of yoga, meditation, journaling, and essential oils. It has been a huge part of my own growth, healing and my story, and I am excited to share that with you.

Thank you for believing in 'you' enough to take this journey with me.

much love,

Lou xo

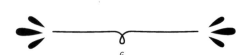

WHO IS LOU

Hello lovelies…. Yes I said it again and I'll keep saying it because if you believe me or not, you are so wonderfully lovely. I coined this phrase years ago as a way to greet others and it's been amazing to watch it move so easily into other peoples vocabulary. Spreading love, both for others but also more importantly towards ourselves is why I started. So who am I? Well that really is the real question that we will all ponder on at some point during our lives or maybe who are we not. I'll have to leave you with knowing that I'm still discovering, uncovering and learning who Lou is. What I can tell you is the bricks and mortar of me, aka the many hats I wear in the lives of those around me.

I am a mama to three real babies and three fur babies. My kids are my biggest teachers and my kitties are my biggest snugglers. I am also a wife and my hubby heralds my fanclub with support and praise for all I choose to do. He is my second and my last. Well I know it happens to so many of us these days, right?! So yes I went through divorce and it was far from heavenly but I'd choose the trials and tribulations all over again to be where I am now. Every challenge has its lessons to be learned and accepted.

I did spend a part of my life as a single mama, so I totally understand the sacrifices that us mamas make for our children and everyone else in our lives.

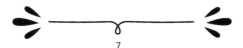

I have had a few paths in life. I was a clothing designer for over a decade working in the UK, Italy, and Canada. I felt drawn, however, to making others feel better and so this led me to yoga training, massage, reiki, meditation, and working with women.

I have to tell you about my mama because she has played a huge role in my life and is why I am where I am now. My mama was the ultimate people pleaser and she was and still is the best at it. The problem with that is that she was doing it to the detriment of herself. She had low self-esteem and so as a little girl I would tell her how amazing she was, she never believed me. She did so much for everyone one, but she just couldn't receive the praise of others. She couldn't see what others saw and numbed out her feelings about herself by being of service to others. This made her feel like she had some sort of value here. So with all that being said, is it any wonder that I grew up to be a people pleaser too.

There are huge problems in being a people pleaser. We often gain our self-worth through the opinions of others. We can begin to thrive on feeling needed and useful at the expense of our own needs. Welcome to overwhelming stress, anxiety, and exhaustion. You may already know them but for a long time they were my friends.

I'm an empath and as such I want to make everyone feel better. I used to say yes to virtually everything even though sometimes I was exhausted spiritually and every other way too. Does this sound like you? This is hard to admit, but as people pleasers we are actually enablers. We allow others to take advantage of us.

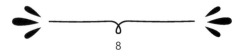

Guess what?! NO is a complete sentence and both my mama and I are learning to have that in our vocabulary now. Learning to love yourself just as you are will allow you to choose what makes you happy first.

My biggest lesson I experienced during my divorce when I truly crashed and burned. The silver lining in hitting rock bottom is that you get to put the pieces back together in a way that serves you. Now I'm not suggesting you have to go to that extreme. I just want you to know that sometimes when life takes us to places we weren't expecting to go, it's for a reason and you get to choose how things move forward. When we believe we are not enough, we don't make time for the things our hearts and souls need. Things that fill our cup and spark our light. Self care is not a luxury ladies, it's a necessity. When we are in a space of truly loving ourselves, living our best and happiest lives becomes our priority. When we have full cups and happy hearts, it is much easier to lift others and serve without losing our own way.

I now start each day in a way that lights me up. I say NO to so much more than I have ever done and I ask myself a lot more questions before I say YES to things. I'm getting braver with daring to show the world truly who I am. I am letting go of pretending to be someone I am not. I'm just Lou and I know now that you can't please everyone nor will everyone like you so it's time to stop trying. It's time to be authentically you. The most important person that needs to, not only like you but love you, is yourself. Nothing or no person is ever perfect, and so we need to learn to love the imperfections of life and ourselves. If we can get to a place where everything is always seen as perfectly imperfect, we can remove the pressures and barriers that stop us from just being.

I .... (name)

DARE TO SPARKLE

Put a picture of you here.

HOW THIS WORKS

Let's start with how we mean to go on during the next 30 days and let's be honest when we also say the rest of our lives. I'm not really asking you to see this as a 'thing' or a fad, but more of a wake-up call.

YOU ARE ENOUGH, YOU ARE MORE THAN ENOUGH.

I also want to put this out there now so that you don't set yourself up to fail. I know you don't think you are 'that' person, but at times we are all that person. We get hugely motivated and set our standards so high that it becomes impossible to achieve. Therefore, I am setting the tone for my expectations for you. If you miss a day—so what?!

Yep, it is something that happens to us all. Super motivated in the beginning, like nothing will stand in our way! Then a few days of life gets totally in the way, like it's testing us, and we get overwhelmed. So my request to you is please don't stop, give up or berate yourself and most importantly don't judge yourself. If you miss a day or even a week, just go back to it when you are ready. This book is to help you create self-love and self-care, so there is no room for the negative narrative.

Also, if you come to a day in the book that is too challenging for you now feel free to miss it and come back to it later. Just promise me, you won't give up on you.

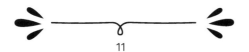

I AM ENOUGH. WHO I AM IS ENOUGH. WHAT I DO IS ENOUGH AND WHAT I HAVE IS ENOUGH.

This is your mantra now. Write it down right now and carry it with you in your purse or bag or put it somewhere you will see it a lot.

It is the truth whether right now you want to believe it or not because each one of us is unique, special and the complete package plus some. We sometimes just forget, lose our way, or find that we have been led astray in life.

I created 'Dare to Sparkle' because I look for the sparkle in myself and in those around me. That sparkle is in all of us and taking the time to nurture ourselves allows us to bask in our own light.

It's not going to be easy, but then growth and change aren't. I want you to commit to you. If you don't, the only person you are letting down is you and you quite frankly should be your number one priority. The only one who can make you happy enough to sparkle for the whole world to see, is you.

Too often I see the light in someone, but they don't see it in themselves and no matter how many times you tell them, not a thing will change until they are ready to do the work. Perhaps even if they do see it, then something stops them from sharing that. Perhaps fear, lack of self-worth or that feeling of I am not enough. Don't feel guilty for how you feel ever. Our journeys have brought us to this point. We can not change the past, but we can change our future.

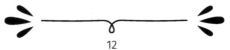

There are 30 activities for 30 days with a couple of bonuses thrown in for good measure.

The idea is to methodically work through the days in order. Try to do one per day but if you need longer, take longer. If you are challenged by an activity as I mentioned before, miss that day and try to come back to it later.

Maybe this will be a solo journey for you or maybe you need to embrace the idea of doing this with a friend, someone you love for motivation and accountability. This book is just the start of a life that puts YOU first, at least for a small part of every single day.

This book is paired with emotional essential oils to guide you through this whole process of ceremony and self-care but can be done without if you don't have them or prefer not to use them.

Essential Oils

Now you might be asking yourself why essential oils? Well from the moment you are born, you are creating connections in your brain between memories and smells. It's a pretty powerful experience for our emotions and our energy body. We are energy. Plants are energy. Together we feel elevated. In fact, humans have a lot of similarities to plants, and we have been using them for centuries to support our physical and emotional health.

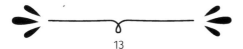

I am suggesting that you use dōTERRA essential oils because it's the only brand I trust for purity and ethicality with my family and clients. Pure therapeutic grade essential oils are not only great for our bodies physically but also energetically and emotionally.

For each day during the program, an oil is suggested for you to use. You could diffuse it, wear it, smell it from the bottle throughout the day, or put it on a diffuser necklace or bracelet.

If you don't have one of the oils, or it's an oil that you do not like, or there is another you would prefer to use, then work with your own inner guide. When you allow your intuition to speak and have its voice, it will guide you to where you need to be.

This program is about nourishing yourself so much that you can't help to radiate and sparkle.

Here is a list of the oils listed in the book:

Spikenard	Smart + Sassy	Lime
Magnolia	Motivate	Roman Chamomile
Black pepper	Breathe/Easy Air	Bergamot
Passion	Lavender	Wild orange
Rose	Jasmine	Cheer
Ylang ylang	Sandalwood	Tangerine
Clary sage	Clove	Ginger
Cedarwood	Grapefruit	Lemon
Patchouli	Lemongrass	Elevation
Peppermint	Eucalyptus	Melissa

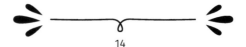

How to use your oils

Aromatical use of oils is one of the quickest ways to work with our emotions. You can smell them directly from the bottle. You can also place a drop or two in the palms of your hands, rub them together and cup your hands. Inhale the aroma for 3 to 5 breaths.

Diffusing your essential oils in a water diffuser is a great way to change the energy of the space you are in and one of my favourite ways to work with oils. It can be fun and playful too as you find combinations that really resonate with you.

Topical use can be varied too. Add 10 drops to Epsom salts or a carrier oil and add them to a deep, warm therapeutic bath. You can add a few drops to a massage cream or fractionated coconut oil and apply it to your skin. Mix a little with a carrier oil and apply like perfume or to your pulse points, the inner creases of your elbow, along the neck or spine or over the heart.

I encourage you to be guided by what feels natural and right for you to do. You might like a ritual of using them in the same way every day or you might decide something different each day. Let this be a whole experiential journey into you.

An extra special gift

I do make oil suggestions throughout the book, but on top of that I have an extra gift to share with you. I love to wear this blend every single day and the name of this book came from the name of this blend. I created 5 years ago called 'Dare to Sparkle' and it took me a year of playing to be happy with it. I wanted women to feel like they could take on the world and sparkle and so this is your sparkle in a bottle.

5 drops Citrus Bliss
2 drops Ginger
1 drop Melissa
1 drop Ylang Ylang

Grab a 10 ml roller bottle and add the above. Top the bottle with fractionated coconut oil. Gently shake and then apply as you would your favourite perfume.

Citrus Bliss—This is a creative and playful oil. Full of motivation and get up and go. It's the sparkle in the blend.

Ginger—This is the bold part of the blend. The part that tells you that you are enough and you can do this. It helps us to find our strength in purpose.

Melissa—This oil is one of my favourites. It is the oil of light and is a reminder to our souls as to their purpose on earth.

Ylang Ylang—This is the feminine and gentle part of the blend. It reminds us to access our inner knowing and be guided by our hearts.

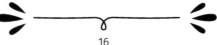

DAY ONE
GET YOUR GRATITUDE ON

Let's start as we mean to go on by creating new healthy habits in our lives that promote the rediscovery of ourselves and how awesome we are. Yes, I did say you are awesome.

The most important part of the journey isn't the beginning or the end, but the wondrous discoveries made along the way." —Patti Ballard.

This is not an overnight fix. For some, this journey will be a lifelong one and for others this spark might reignite them and their passion so as to inspire others in their life.

Why start with gratitude? Well when we are grateful for everything in our lives that includes gratitude for ourselves and our lives. Focusing on the positive lessens the negative!

Are you ready to discover the magic that is within you and around you?

Let's start with GRATITUDE.

Today's oil is spikenard - the oil of gratitude.◊

What you love, you empower.

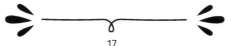

Tip: Try applying 1 to 2 drops to the hands and taking 3 or 4 nice deep breaths. You could also try diffusing it with a few drops of geranium.

Firstly, I want you to head outside and find your rock. Not to sit on silly. To hold. Small enough to fit into your palm with your fingers wrapped around it.

Mine found me in a very random turn of events. A beach I'd never heard of at the end of a 4-hour coach journey to a place I'd never knew existed. There is a little more to it but you get the gist. I have random parents who would take me to random places. The beach was a stone beach and one particular stone caught my eye. I was so obvious too. Like 'hello Lou! Here I am!' It was unlike any rock I have ever seen before or since. So I promise you that you will know when you find yours.

Take your time to find it. It could be a regular stone or a crystal. It doesn't really matter although crystals have meanings of their own too, which can be awesome. What matters though is that it calls you to it and as long as it brings you joy when you see it and hold it, then all is good. The point of it is for you to be drawn to it and love it so that it is a constant reminder of your gratitude practice.

Off you go and when you have it I'll meet you back here.

Now that the hard part is done, let's get on with what I want you to do with your precious little rock.

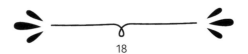

Place your rock or crystal next to your bed on your night stand, if you have one or where you will see it every morning and every night.

Tonight will be the start of your journey to rewire the way you see life and see yourself. When you go to sleep tonight and every night after, you will hold your rock in your hand and think about the one thing you were most grateful for in your day; if you'd like, you can also write this down in your journal. This method of focusing on the thing you are most grateful for allows you to relive all the wonderful joys you received throughout the entire day in order to find your favourite. This leaves you drifting off to sleep with a mind filled with happy thoughts.

But, hey your gratitude habits don't end there. When you wake in the morning and before your feet even touch the floor, I want you to also choose 3 things that you are grateful for as your day begins. Again, if you choose to intensify this practice, you can write these 3 down.

Fostering an attitude of gratitude in our lives will help us to appreciate the things in our life that we often miss or take for granted.

This is where the magic begins.

DAY TWO
POSITIVE POST-ITS

There are often negative aspects of our life, or negative people and/or situations that can really affect our mojo. Our confidence can take a beating and our self-worth can need a boost. Sometimes the negativity is in our own words and our thoughts. We aren't born this way, but we learn quickly to accept these untruths.

Dear self, today you will SHINE !!!!

Today's task is to help you manifest how you want to feel in life. It's the start of our personal language of love and encouragement to ourselves. Without love for ourselves, we cannot truly share love with others.

Grab yourself a book of post-its and start to write kind words to yourself. Choose to uplift and empower each day with high vibrational words of love and worthiness.

Positive affirmations are powerful and when we surround ourselves with them, then we can begin to create a shift in our perception of ourselves.

Today's oil is magnolia - the oil of compassion.

Keep shining beautiful one, the world needs your light.

Tip: I love to roller this one on like perfume. Behind my ears, on my heart, my inner wrists and the inner creases of my elbows.

Here are a few to get you started:

- The world needs me.

- I am creating my life.

- I am confident.

- I am courageous.

- I am enough.

- I am open.

- I choose love.

- I am creative.

- I am smart.

- I am beautiful.

- I am lovable.

- I am funny.

- I am worthy.

Now stick these notes to yourself anywhere and every-where that you will see them. Perhaps on the bathroom mirror, in your car, your wallet, your computer screen, and even the fridge. Make a conscious intention today to read them and be present.

Write below how they make you feel. I want you to commit to reading them every day. Go back to this page when you have finished this book too and revisit those feelings.

Write how you feel today...

Write how you feel after a month...

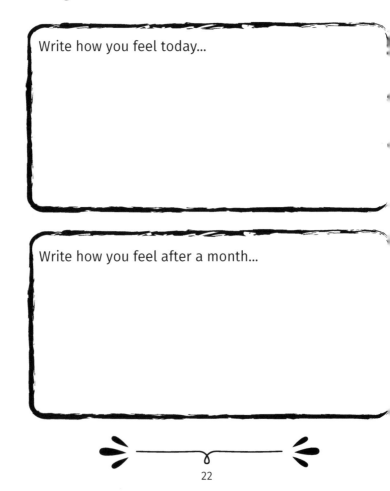

DAY THREE
10 NOT SO SWEET THINGS

Isn't it so easy to put ourselves down, to judge, berate and generally say not so sweet things about ourselves. Why do we do that? It really is just too easy to be harder on ourselves than we would be on anyone else. We set ourselves up to fail before we have even started. READ THAT AGAIN. We set ourselves up to fail before we have even started. Hello self-sabotage!

The moment is now, not tomorrow, or yesterday or someday. Right here. Right now. This is your moment to shine.

If we want the story of our lives to change, then we must be willing to change what we do to get a different out-come. Change the narrative and get a different ending.

Today we are going to start with the easy. The 'not so sweet things' because it is way easier to talk about what we don't like about ourselves than what we do. Phew, I hear you say but hey it's not going to be that simple. We need to figure out what we are working with here.

Today's oil is black pepper – the oil of unmasking. ◊

A negative mind will never give you a positive life.

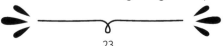

23

Tip: Add the following to your diffuser and put it on while you do this next exercise.

4 drops Black pepper
3 drops Grapefruit
2 drops Lemon

So on the next page I want you to write out a list of 10 things that you do not like about yourself. Likely, there will be a lot of physical things that you will focus on because that is what us ladies do very well. For some reason we really don't like talking our own looks or bodies in a positive or kind way, but that stops now. We are going to rewrite our stories and internal dialogue slowly, but surely, one unkind word at a time.

In an effort to identify what our hang-ups are, though, we need to actually say them out loud. It's a process in which we can learn to flip that negativity on its head.

f you need more space or you don't want to write in
your book, grab a journal or a piece of paper.

1 _

2 _

3 _

4 _

5 _

6 _

7 _

8 _

9 _

10 _

So here they are in black and white. Those terrible things
you have been thinking and saying to yourself for years.

How does seeing it make you feel?

Now I want you to go back to your list and see how you can take each of your negative comments and turn them around in some way; even if you can only manage a glimmer of positivity it's still a start.

For example, I don't like the way my nose looks. It's too big, I don't like the shape or I wish it was different. How about instead you focus on its benefits. Imagine if you didn't even have a nose. So try…. My nose lets me smell the flowers, the warm air on a summer day, and the apple pie cooking in the oven.

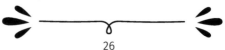

Without my nose and sense of smell I'd miss out on so many memories and experiences that I am reminded of each time I inhale.

Maybe one of the things you don't like is being an introvert and having a hard time meeting friends. We can flip this on its head too by noticing that in being an introvert you are likely more attentive to the friends you do have. You may keep friendships longer because you have more dialogue on the inside, so you are much more careful with your words.

We can literally find positives for every negative we can think about ourselves. I want you to find benefits for the 10 things you wrote on the previous page and write them below.

1 _____

2 _____

3 _____

4 _____

5 _____

6 _

7 _

8 _

9 _

10 _

How do you feel now? Can you see a glimmer of light?

DAY FOUR
GRATITUDE JOURNAL

So you should now be getting in the habit of daily gratitudes with your little gratitude rock, that you started
with on day 1.

Happiness can be found even in the darkest of
times. If only one, remembers to turn on the
light. —Albus Dumbledore.

It's time to make those gratitudes a permanent reminder
of just how sweet life can be. When we focus on the
positives instead of the negatives, we can see just how
illuminating this can be to our hearts and souls. Also,
when we focus on the positives, there literally is no room
for negativity.

Make this whole task super special. What I mean by that
is: be intentional. Buy or find a beautiful notebook instead of a scrap of paper or any old notebook. Find a pen
that feels special too.

Place them somewhere, you will see them every day. I
like to put mine next to my bed and start to make this a
habit, a routine.

Today's oil is passion - the oil of creativity.

It's time to stop pretending you're this average
person, you've got big work to do. BIG. —Tiffany Han.

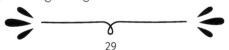

29

Tip: This oil smells AMAZING! It is great used in your diffuser to fill the space you are in. It can also be used on your skin. A little dab on the pulse points or add a drop or two to your favourite body lotion and apply liberally. If you want to get extra creative, diffuse and apply!

You will need to make time at the end of the day in a quiet space, so you don't feel rushed. You will likely only need a couple of minutes each day to do this. It may take a little longer in the beginning until this becomes ha-bitual. Starting to write is always the hardest part of this task, so just put pen to paper and start writing anything. Whatever pops up into your head, big or small, that makes you feel thankful. If it's easier, just write points or single words rather than sentences. It doesn't have to be perfect or well written or momentous things. Some days you might find are harder, especially if your day was challenging. These are the days when I am thankful for the earth, or my breath or my tears.

Everything we experience is part of our journey. It is a chance to grow, learn, and bloom.

To be a star you must shine your own light, follow your own path and don't worry about the darkness for that is when the stars shine brightest.
—Ralph Waldo Emerson.

Personally I love to write what I am grateful for and then go into the little extra details of why. It makes it much more enjoyable when you are having a day of recollection and you can go back to your journal and relive those experiences all over again. Maybe instead you find you need some inspiration and past days bring you that and so much more. The written word is a powerful catalyst for a change of mindset, so when you reread your journal, especially on a more challenging day, you get to feel the love and light.

Try to keep this journal going up for the rest of the 30 days and beyond. When we can find an attitude of gratitude, we can literally turn the world on its head. We can see that life is happening for us and not to us or against us.

One tip I have is to not be too intense with dating the days in your journal. When we miss days, it can become really obvious if we do. We can then easily circle into a place of judgment and expectations on ourselves. Remember the part we chatted over already about setting ourselves up to fail. Well we don't want to do any of that. The whole premise of this book is to help us feel good about who we are inside and out. Also, to help us have a positive mindset that focuses on us being enough as opposed to nothing ever being perfect. These tools are to help us keep moving forward in life.

DAY FIVE
BLESSING MEDITATION

There are many ways to uplift our lives and the lives of those around us. When we feel good about ourselves, it is much easier to share that light with others to lift and inspire them. When we don't feel so great about ourselves, then everything can be a drain on our energy and spirit. So counting our blessings is a way we can take time for ourselves and focus our minds on what we can control. There is much in life that we can't, however we can control how we react and where we choose to channel our attention.

You are a miracle. You are a perfect combination that makes you *you*. Let yourself shine bright.

Today you are going to find a comfortable place to be for a little while. It can be on the floor, a chair, a bed, or anywhere where you won't be disturbed for 10 minutes. You can use cushions or blankets too. Take your time to make a sacred space.

Today's oil is rose - the oil of divine love.

You have to find what sparks a light in you so that you in your own way can illuminate the world. —Oprah Winfrey.

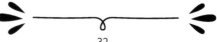

Now close your eyes and begin to watch your breath. Relax your tummy and feel the inhale, fill it up as the exhale lets it relax. Don't force it. Just become observant.

We tend to hold our breath, and we take shallow inhales especially when we are stressed. Remember no judgement, just be present.

We are going to use the mantra—that means a repetition of words—LET GO. Breathe in the word LET as you allow calm and love and beauty to enter and GO as you breathe out anything that isn't serving you.

As you feel your body start to relax and your mind quieten, then we can move on to counting our blessings. You can start by visualizing the people in your life, situations and anything that makes you feel grateful. On your inhale, visualize whatever it might be and as you exhale either silently say: "thank you" or whisper it. The easiest way to start is to choose things that are easy to be grateful for. However, we all know that it is the more difficult things in our life that challenge the very heart of our self-confidence and acceptance. Over time, you will be able to find gratitude for those things too because it is all part of our journey.

Tip: I love drawing this oil on my heart. Maybe a heart on a heart or a hug and a kiss. Also, the pulse points and alone the back of the neck. Make sure you roller some on your palms and take 3 or 4 nice deep breaths before you get started.

How did that make you feel?

Share some of your blessings here:

DAY SIX
SILLY SELFIE

Wow! When did we get all boring and stuck? No seriously.... I wonder at what age we just decided that's it.
I am done being a child and having fun and being playful? I don't want to stand out. I want to just blend in and
not be noticed. The idea of being like sheep, because
fitting in is easier than standing out.

When did we start getting so conscious of what other's
might think of us and our actions that we let that take
precedence over being weird, wild, and fun! The spontaneity of being a kid took us into all kinds of fun places
and experiences until we let fear and rejection in. Well
now it's time to revisit our brave and fearless selves. Remember what other people think of you is none of your
business.

Take a breather and do something fun!!

So this might be something you do a lot or something
that the very thought of it makes you cringe. Either way I
am going to ask you to do this anyway.

Today's oil is ylang ylang –
the oil of the inner child.

She leaves a little sparkle wherever she goes.

35

Tip: Try putting this oil on your body and taking some nice breaths. Find some of your favourite music. Dance and move. Smile and loosen up. I want to create your carefree vibe so that you can get down and get silly!! Remember when you were a child and you had no cares or worry; when peer pressure was a foreign word to you. That's what I am after.

I want you to take a fun selfie. No, I don't want you to take 60 shots until you find the one that you think is OK or is staged so that you look "good". Have fun with it. Be silly and spontaneous. Pull funny faces, strike a pose and be the real you. The 5-year-old you! Find the magic.

Even better, do this with a friend or loved one and let them take your selfies. You can do the same for them. Sometimes we are less reluctant to have fun and embrace our goofy sides if we have someone in our corner being just as daft and vulnerable.

Now if you are feeling really brave, I want you to post your picture on social media and encourage others to be spontaneous and adventurous. If that feels like a step too far, then instead I want you to choose one of your pictures to print out and add to the next page.

Take some time to experience how you felt before, during, and afterwards. Processing the way our minds think and sabotage us is part of this learning process.

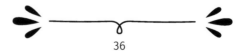

Post your picture below. I know you can be brave and do this.

How did this task make you feel before?

How did this task make you feel during?

How did this task make you feel after?

DAY SEVEN
10 THINGS I LOVE ABOUT ME

OK, so we have kind of visited this already, but I let you work on the negative things that you think about yourself first. For some reason that is much easier, which seems so strange to me when as humans our natural state is to be happy. Perhaps we have taken ourselves to a place that we believe we are not deserving of that happiness. I am here to tell you that you are and so much more. You deserve a boat load of self-worth, self-love, and self-care.

Beautiful girl you were made to do hard things so believe in yourself.

You have the whole 30 days to complete this because I know it's the hardest thing that I will ask you to likely do. So today start with at least 3 things, that right now you love about you. Some of your 10 should definitely talk about you physically. It's not called ego or boasting but SELF-LOVE.

Today's oil is clary sage –
the oil of clarity and vision.◊

Your past does not predict your future so start by forgiving yourself when you go to beat yourself up.

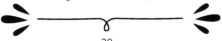

Tip: Try diffusing this oil and create a space for yourself to work on this. Maybe add a few drops of lavender to help you feel relaxed but also to find your voice.

10 things I love about ME:

1 -

2 -

3 -

4 -

5 -

6 -

7 -

8 -

9 -

10 -

DAY EIGHT
JUST SAY THANK YOU

Have you ever noticed that when you receive a compliment, you feel the need to discredit it? Someone says your hair looks great and you answer 'I washed it'. Someone compliments your outfit and you reply 'oh this? I got it at the charity store'. Or something to that effect. When we don't believe we are amazing, beautiful, shining, sparkly, awesome, just as we are, then we wonder how could someone else see what we can't.

We are stars wrapped in skin - the light you are seeking has always been within.

You may have not believed the person who paid you the compliment or you may be trying to be humble. What you are actually doing is stealing from someone. Think of it this way. The person who complimented you felt good doing it and then you have taken that experience away from them. You stole their thunder and you made it about you but that wasn't your role to play.

Today's oil is cedarwood - the oil of community.°

Don't be afraid to sparkle a little brighter !!

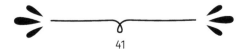

I know why you did it because if you had accepted it, you would have had to sit with the feeling that you didn't deserve to get that compliment. Perhaps that you feel like you don't deserve to feel happy and good about who you are. Have you ever stopped to think for a minute that maybe you are telling yourself a narrative that doesn't exist anywhere else except in your head. Have you ever considered that you really do deserve all the praise and recognition that the world has to offer and then some.

All new habits take time and an adjustment period. You've heard of the expression that 'Rome wasn't built in a day'. Well, neither was your self-worth or self-love and respect for yourself. I am challenging you to start the change and feel uncomfortable for a while.

I am preparing you to be seen and allow others to be seen too. You might be an introvert like me but I can assure you it is worth it. The friendships and inner confidence I have received from stepping out of my comfort zone and connecting to others has been a two-way street. It wasn't easy at all, but real change isn't. It's discomfort on so many levels.

Today's exercise is two-fold. You are going to pay compliments to others including at least one perfect stranger.

I always find complimenting a stranger is an easier way of connecting with them than picking a random topic and trying to start up dialogue.

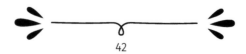

Step two is acceptance. The part where you start to receive. Accepting the compliments is a huge step. So anytime anyone says something complimentary to you, the only thing you are allowed to say is THANK YOU! That's it... don't push it away, don't add to it, just digest it and smile.

You can read Day 9 for more on this as this is your task for tomorrow. However, in the process of giving compliments, you may receive some too, so I want you to be prepared.

You can also choose to do Days 8 and 9 together if you prefer.

Tip: We are creating community and light all around us. Try using this oil on your feet to ground yourself and feel connected. You could diffuse this oil with lavender while you take the time to share your light and love with others.

OK so back to sharing your light with others so that they may feel better about themselves. You can say, text, email, video call, your messages to those you want to share with.

If it's easier, start with those closest to you. Who can you think of that would appreciate a little more love and acknowledgement in their lives.

I love to spend an hour randomly texting friends and how amazing I think they are. I know if you try this, you are going to be blown away with how good this feels and what you actually receive in return.

Take a moment to acknowledge how good it feels to make someone else feel this way and know that you can also make someone else experience that same inner glow by accepting what they are offering too.

Write down the compliments you give:

1 _____

2 _____

3 _____

4 _____

5 _____

6 _____

7 _____

8 _____

9 _____

10 _____

Who did you compliment:

How did it make you feel?

How did they respond?

Did anyone deflect your compliment and if so how did that make you feel?

What was your favourite compliment experience and why?

DAY NINE
WOW ANOTHER COMPLIMENT!?

Frankly we just don't remember the good stuff. Why is that? It's easier for us to put ourselves down or judge or berate, than it is to give ourselves a pat on the back or speak to ourselves with kindness. We have been convinced by society that we aren't enough. That we are lacking. Now that is crazy! But we are told that loving yourself is being full of it and having a big ego. We are taught that it is wrong to be happy with who we are. So we learn to see the flaws and the faults and not the beauty and the wonder of life and us.

Maybe if we photograph it or video it or write about the good stuff, we might start to embrace it. But, really how much of what we share is authentic? Did we blur the vision or doctor the story? We have grown somewhat to love misery. To believe that when things are going great, that something is going to happen to change that. We self-sabotage. Again we come back to our non-belief in our ability to be enough. When we actually deserve all the happiness that we have the capacity to imagine.

Today's oil is patchouli - the oil of physicality. ◊

Each of us shines in a different way but this doesn't make our light and less bright.

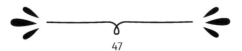

Generally, it is easier for all of us though to remember what went wrong or what someone said that wasn't very nice. It is much easier for us to put ourselves down and believe hurtful words than it is to accept kind complimentary words. It's because most of us struggle with believing that we are worthy, and we haven't figured out how amazing we are yet.

Read this part twice or more if you need to. For this whole rest of the program and beyond, when someone says something nice to you, you will simply say, thank you, and then write it down. Don't get lazy! Every single time you receive praise! Got it? Promise me you will. If it helps write yourself a reminder or take a little notebook with you. It's truly amazing how many compliments you will receive in just a month if you are paying attention.

Tip: We are working with very heart-centred work here. Try taking 4 to 5 deep breaths of this oil from your palms and then take a moment to apply the oil to your heart. Place your hands on your heart and guide your breath, self-love and pace here.

I want you to start to see yourself as others see you. This is not a quick fix though for most of us. It will take time, practice, and patience with yourself. We are our own worst critics, and we set the bar for ourselves so far out of reach that it will never be attainable unless we give ourselves a break. So this means having to create new healthy habits that we can use as tools to help us rewire our unhealthy thoughts.

You are definitely going to start catching yourself in your old patterns and know that is OK. It's part of the process. I love to think of it as the analogy of the butterfly who can't see how beautiful her wings are but everyone else can. I don't want you to lose yourself anymore in how you think you are or how you believe other people (who aren't in your tribe) think of you. The judgemental, not happy in their life ones.... We all have them. What they think is not relevant. What others think is none of your concern. The only person that has to live with you and the life you create is you. As my guru would say, "mind your own business." Basically focus on yourself and getting your own house in order and let others do them—unless of course they are paying you a giant compliment.

So don't reject, push away or try to play down the compliment you are being given. Also don't try to 'up' them on it either. What I mean by this is when someone tells you your hair looks amazing and you say but yours looks better. I know you might want to use any or all of these deflections but don't. I want you to feel and notice your resistance and move through it. I did tell you that some of this will be challenging. Think of it this way. When you reject praise, you are actually stealing love, joy, and light that was meant for the person saying the words to you. Let them have their moment and who knows you might have one too.

Write down the compliments given to you:

You can not blend in when you were meant to shine. Be a light.

DAY TEN
LET'S GET BENDY

Maybe you are a yoga nut already like me, or maybe the very thought of getting bendy sends you running in the opposite direction. Today's self-love comes in the form of being present with yourself and your body, just as it is right now. No judgement please.

I hear the words uttered too many times from women I work with that they will be happy when they have lost weight or get into shape. Yoga helps us to go deeper spiritually and see the wonderful light that each of us has and that isn't governed by dress size. When we start to love ourselves, we naturally become more active. We tend to feed our bodies nutritious food because we start to care more and that in itself can have beautiful benefits.

So get yourself to a class today or put on your favourite video or head to YouTube. There is every style you can imagine and it's all free. I don't care if you choose a short, long, fast, or slow class. Whatever you can manage.

Today's oil is peppermint –
the oil of a buoyant heart.

You can not blend in when you were meant to
shine. Be a light.

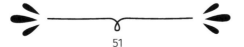

51

Tip: Try placing a drop of your peppermint oil between your palms and inhaling deeply before you start. It is fabulous for helping you to feel connected, present, and energized. It also opens up the airways so you can take nice deep breaths during your yoga class. Just be careful not to get peppermint too close to your eyes.

If you find yourself enjoying this time for you and moving your body, I want you to commit to once or twice a week. You might have found that certain poses felt wonderful in your body, so it's quite alright to stick to the poses you love to begin with. I do find that the poses that I don't like quite so much are the ones that take me on a greater adventure of self-discovery.

I always add a little yoga at the end of my morning workout because it just feels so good to stretch out and let go. We are often not aware of just where all our tension is hiding. Slowing down and listening to what our body is saying is a very healthy way to live. Our bodies are a perfect treasure trove of trapped emotions which over we can start to release.

Now you have finished your session, take a moment to pause. Whether you enjoyed it or not, I'm really proud that you gave it a try. Whether you just did a little intentional breathing or a full yoga practice, I'd like to sit for a while with how you felt before, during, and after.

Write your thoughts below or even single words that represent your experience.

How did you feel before? Physically and emotionally.

How did you feel during?

How did you feel after?

DAY ELEVEN
DRESS TO IMPRESS

Who do you normally dress for? Maybe a dress code at work, maybe to find a partner or for your partner? Maybe you already dress for yourself. Do you really feel good? If yes! Fantastic—you got this. I find that my dress sense follows my mind. If I don't feel good about myself, I wear comfies and baggy clothes so I can hide away. If I am feeling good, then I take more time to find the clothes that make me feel good too.

Some girls are just born with glitter in their veins

Dress to impress is about dressing to make yourself feel good and not for anyone else. It's not limited to clothes either. Maybe you feel amazing when you have had your hair done, or eyelashes or nails. Maybe it is going and buying a new outfit or a pair of shoes.

I always find a huge difference when I put on really sassy underwear and not my 'old faithfuls'. No-one knows I have them on but I do and it makes me feel good. Also sparkles and sequins are my go-tos whenever I can!

Today's oil is smart + sassy –
the oil of inner beauty.

I stopped looking for the light and decided to
become it instead.

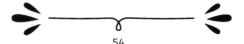

Tip: Try diffusing this yummy oil. It's also an amazing oil for helping us to feel content and satiated. Well ladies, most of us are emotional eaters, so this not only helps that but lifts the spirits with its uplifting and cheerful smell.

So today, dress for the you, you want to be. The amazing 'sure of yourself you'; even if it just starts at home. It's time to make an effort for you because it's your life you are living. You deserve all the love you have to offer. Start a love affair with yourself!

I am going to add a little note here. Day 24 might be a big help here to make this a more enjoyable experience if your closet has too many past items that just don't fit right now. What I am referring to here is something the majority of women do. We buy clothes and then even if they don't fit anymore, we keep them. We are hoping that one day they will fit again, but what we are actually doing is torturing ourselves. Now if you are wanting to keep some because you like the motivation factor, then that's fantastic if that is how it makes you feel. However, if you are mentally judging and beating yourself up every time you see the little black dress or the skinny jeans, it might be time for them to go. If an item in any way is holding you back in the self-worth category, then let it go. Pair down your closet to the items that you love and that also make you feel great when you wear them.

Write down a few things that make you feel happy about what you wear and how you want to feel and look.
This will help you to create your inner and outer shopping list. If right now you are finding this super challenging that's OK. It's normal. Focus on writing about how you want to feel and identifying what helps you feel like you can rock the world.

So start your list of things that make you feel fabulous. It can include things that you like to do like wearing mascara, or drying your hair straight or painting your nails as well as items of clothing and accessories. Maybe you have always wanted to wear the perfect hat?!

DAY TWELVE
GET MOVING

Get out of your head and into your body. Moving your body not only improves cardiovascular health, but it improves cerebrovascular health too. A wide range of recent studies have found that exercise improves brain function, structure, and connectivity. These brain improvements are directly linked to improved learning, memory, and cognitive function.

Your only limit is you.

You are the only one that can come up with excuses. And I have heard them all before because I have used most of them.

Health and happiness that sounds like an amazing reason to start right?! We get to live longer, be smarter, and sassier because moving our bodies gives us a natural high and does wonders for our self-worth.

A friend once said, treat your body with care because you love it, not because you hate it. If we can truly learn to love this vehicle of a body that we have been gifted.

Today's oil is motivate - the oil of motivation.°

Repeat after me 'I can do this!'

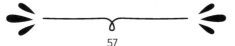

We will feed it well both physically and emotionally. We will move to keep supple and strong. We will treat our body and our mind with love and reverence. I want you to begin to realize that you have the power to be what you want to be. Don't doubt how amazing and strong you are.

However, I don't want to make it too easy on you either. Some of you may already be doing lots of moving. I also know, however, that some of you are not. Let me be the first to say there is absolutely no judgement here. Life is full of ebbs and flows and falling in love with moving can be one of them.

I do want you to get out of your comfort zone though and try something new! Belly-dancing, swimming, ballet, trail running.... Even walking to the store instead of driving counts. Drag a friend with you if you need back up but most importantly make an effort because the effort is all on you and you might need telling but you are so very worth it.

Tip: This oil is a yummy combo of citrus and mint oils which are known for their ability to lift our spirits, increase our energy, and get us focused. Try diffusing this while you are getting ready to go out and hen applying to the pulse points. Also, try a drop on your chest so you can smell while working out.

Start to take back the health of your body and your mind.

Write down a few new you things you are going to try:

What did you choose to do today?

How did you feel before, emotionally and physically?

How did it make you feel during the activity?

How did you feel afterwards, emotionally and physically?

DAY THIRTEEN
TAKE A BREATHER

Do you ever sit or stand still long enough to be aware of your breath? Do you notice how you breathe and how you are holding your body? Are you holding breath right now? Are you breathing fast or slow? Shallow or deep? Does it flow with ease or is it a struggle?

Be free. When you control everything, you enjoy nothing. Sometimes you just need to relax, breathe, let go, and just live in the moment.

So today you are going to take what I call a 'breather'. You have to commit to doing this at least 3 times today. We take our breath for granted, but it has the power to instill big physical shifts and emotional changes in our body.

Give yourself 3 to 5 minutes to just sit somewhere without interruption. Breathe in slowly and then breath out and watch your breath. Breathing in the word 'Let' and breathing out the word 'go'. Allow your focus to be on your breath. Let your body relax, especially your belly. Placing your hands on your belly can be a physical reminder to keep the body relaxed.

Today's oil is Breathe / Easy Air - the oil of breath.

Dream Big - Sparkle More - Shine Bright.

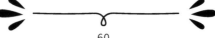

We all have a moment in this busy world we are living in when we need a little more help to relax, ground, be connected, feel safe, and supported.

If you ever find yourself super challenged emotionally, then here is an extra breather tool to help you calm things down.

Sit comfortably. Relax your belly. Feel your lower body connected to the earth. Place one hand on your heart and one hand on your belly. First, notice your breath. Watch it move in and out. Relax your body. Now begin to count the breath on the way in and on the way out. Likely one will be longer than the other. Now try to equalize them. For example, if your breath out is the count of 6 and your breath in is 4, then do both in and out as 4. Try this for about 5 minutes.

Tip: This oil is amazing for soothing our lungs and opening out airways. Try diffusing this in the room you are doing the breathwork. You can also apply a drop to the palms of your hands, tub together and take 4 or 5 nice long deep breaths. This also works for a quick stop and breathe technique when we just need a moment to catch our breath physically and emotionally.

Notice how you were feeling before and after, write it down.

Before you did the breathing exercise, how did you feel?

After you did the breathing exercise, how did you feel?

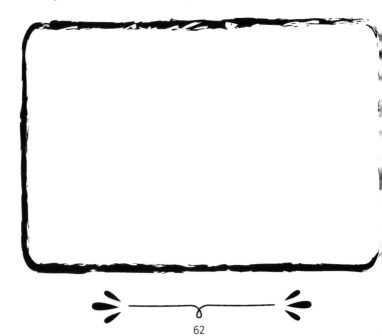

DAY FOURTEEN
WEATHER REPORT

This is something I used to teach teens to do when they came to my yoga classes. It was a great tool for them to begin to understand where their feelings were coming from. To be honest, I think it's something us grown-ups need too. Feelings can be overwhelming and consuming, leaving little room to investigate where they really are coming from and why. That is, unless we choose to play the student in our own life. We are much more than our emotions, but we can learn so much about ourselves when we use them to dig a little deeper. Why was I triggered? Why did that event upset me ? Why am I feeling challenged? When we can be open to exploring our emotions, then we can discover the truth and origin of them. Allowing us to begin to move forward in life with grace and ease.

Get comfortable with being uncomfortable sometimes.

Perhaps taking the time to think about your feelings also will give you the chance to forgive yourself and let go. We all have feelings and that's normal, but how we react is something we can learn to get better at.

Today's oil is lavender - the oil of calm and communication. ◊

Continue growing, learning, evolving and participating in the world.

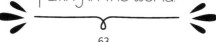

How this works: put an emotion in each quarter of the circle that you are feeling today. In the same quarter, outside of the circle, write why you feel that way. It might sound like a super simple exercise because it is. However, we often make life really complicated, so take the time to get to the bottom of how and why you are feeling the way you are today.

Try this whenever your emotions seem to be getting the better of you to help give you clarity and support.

Tip: Try applying lavender to the heart and the throat.

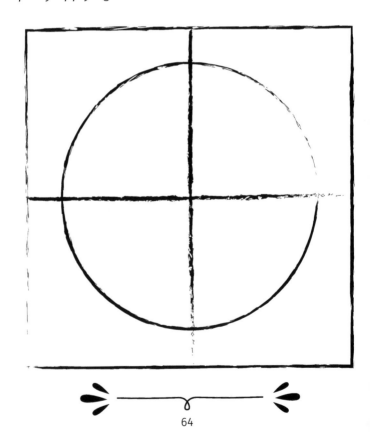

DAY FIFTEEN
SELF-CARE SUNDAY

Let's start by explaining that although the name of this day is catchy, it doesn't really need to be Sunday to do this. Sunday does tend to be a slower day which lends itself to doing things that are just for you, instead of everyone else. However, any day can be self-care day and eventually every day should be. The only person who can put you first and make you happy is you! Also, a little reminder here. Self-care is not a luxury. It is a necessity.

Self-care is not about self-indulgence, it's about self-preservation. —**Audrey** Lorde.

We will start off slowly though and start with today. I want you to factor in doing something for yourself at least twice a week during these next two weeks. If you want to do more, please be my guest. Remember we are working towards every single day.

Today's oil is jasmine –
the oil of balance and trust.◊

It's a good day to take care of yourself
(and so is every other day)

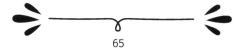

What is self-care? Well, this really can be different for every person because we are each so beautiful and individual. It comes down to what makes you feel happy and content. What fills your cup back up.

Despite the differences in what self-care may be for you, there is one common sabotage to it mastering it and that is time. We tell ourselves we don't have enough time to do all the things we need to do daily, so squeezing self-care in is impossible. Am I right? I know I am because I have heard the excuses from my own self as well as for too many others. What we are actually saying is that we do not matter and that the time spent on ourselves is not time well spent.

I am here to tell you that it is time well spent and it is necessary! Stop doubting that you are worth everything you dream of in your life. You deserve it all and so much more. How can we be of any use to anyone if we don't put a priority on our own well-being. Have you ever wondered why, more than ever, our society is perpetually busy but nothing much actually gets achieved? It's time to slow down and prioritize your life. You do not have to be everything and everyone to those around you. Boundaries are important. What things in your life are eating your time but don't bring you joy? We will dig a little deeper into this later in the book. For now, just make the commitment to some 'you' time.

I mentioned before but I will repeat myself as this is important. We should be giving ourselves self-care every single day even if they are mini moments. So today try to do at least one thing for yourself.

Here are some ideas to get you started. I have also left space for you to add your own. Get creative.

- Go for a walk/run/hike.
- Get pampered - hair, nails, skin.
- Take a long bath (wine and candles.)
- Have a massage.
- Home spa do-it-yourself.
- Meet a friend for coffee, lunch, dinner.
- Take a class just for fun.
- Unplug for an hour.
- Read a book.
- Listen to music.
- Take a nap.
- Have a yummy treat.
- Enjoy a lie in.
- A day in pjs.
- Have a self date.
- Go to the movies.
- Take a little trip.
- Yoga.
- Splurge and get yourself a little something.
- Meditation.
- Girls get together.
- Go to the gym.

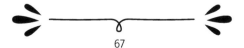

List some things that bring joy to your heart:

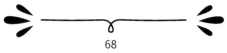

DAY SIXTEEN
DREAMS COME TRUE

Do you believe in magic? As kids, we did. We believed in all kinds of wonderful stuff, the tooth fairy, Santa, and fairies in the garden. Then we grew up and let our head tell us that it didn't exist because how could magic and miracles be real. Instead, we filled our head with problems and worries and beliefs of not being good enough.

You're a miracle. You're the perfect combination that makes you!

Have you ever taken time to think about what your dreams are for yourself. Maybe you visit those aspirations every day. If you don't it's time to create your happy, whatever that might be.

There are a couple ways you can go about this. You can either start a vision board or a dream journal. If you have ever thought about a dream, it deserves to be heard, written, and given its chance to grow, bloom, and evolve. Visualization is the most powerful mind exercise that you can do.

Today's oil is sandalwood – the oil of sacred devotion. °

Dream Big. Be Bold. Be Brave. Be You!

Dream Journal

Choose a notebook that you already love, treasure, cherish, or even buy a new one. One that makes you smile and light up every time you see it. Find a pen you love too. The intention and practice are as important as what you write in the book. I want your dreams to become a habitual practice as you begin to manifest the things you want and deserve.

On each page at the top, write a dream, a wish, a desire you want to happen in your life. Add a picture as well if you would like. Put the date next to the wish and then move on to the next. Visit your journals often to read through them or to add more. When one dream happens then fill in the details and the date. Sometimes you will forget what you wrote and suddenly find that you have made one of your dreams come true. Manifesting and creating the life you want is very magical, but it takes intention on your part, focus and knowing that you very much deserve everything you desire.

Another way you can work with this is to write about your dreams and goals as if they have already happened. Pay attention to how that makes you feel and write those feelings too. Visit every detail of this in your imagination and then make it come alive in your journal.

Either way you decide to do this, you are making your wishes and dreams known to the universe.

Tip: Sandalwood is a beautiful, calming, and grounding oil. It feels like a soft whisper to me. As you set your space up to be creative, think of diffusing this oil with lavender, jasmine, or geranium.

Vision Board

So how does this work? People have been using visualization for years to manifest the things they want in their life.

I have to say I seriously look forward to doing mine every year as an homage to the year ahead. A fresh start. As the new year dawns, I like to re-evaluate what still needs to be on my board and what needs to change. You can choose to follow what suits you though.

It should be based around how you want to do it, after all these are your dreams you are manifesting. You should be considering not only what do you want in your life physically but also how you want to feel in your life.

You are creating a visual image of the life that you want and an image that you are going to see every day. You are also going to place it in your home in a space that you will regularly visit. To really activate your vision board, I would take a few minutes every day to look at everything you have included.

What you will need:

A board—can be one big one or several little ones. It can be paper, cardboard, or a cork board. Anything that you can attach images too and that you can display so you will see it.

Collect magazines, photos, and images of things that you like or that inspire you. Also, words and phrases you like. You might like to add fun markers, embellishments, sparkles, and more.

Have some scissors, glue, tape, or pins handy.

Also, leave yourself a few hours to do this without distraction. (Glass of wine—optional.) No TV. Maybe some nice music. Once you get started, you won't want to stop until it's done.

What goes on your board?

Well, that is really up to you. There is no right or wrong answer, so there is no way to mess this up which makes it even more fun! Put on your board anything that motivates or inspires you in life. The purpose of creating a vision board is to bring all your goals and dreams to fruition. You might want to include relationships, career and finances, home, travel, personal growth (including spirituality, social life, education), and health.

Now go and have fun! Dare to dream big. ♥

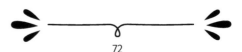

DAY SEVENTEEN
FIND YOUR TRIBE

Who do you surround yourself with? Now I'm not telling you to ditch your family or friends, but it might be time to explore, reach out and begin to find like—minded souls. It might also be the time to set boundaries and limitations on the time you spend or give out to those who don't lift you up.

Be around the light bringers, the magic makers, the world shifters, the game shakers. They will challenge you, break you open, uplift you, and expand you. They won't let you play small with your life. These heart-cen-tred people are your people. These people are your tribe.

Creating healthy boundaries in your life helps you to step out of a place of powerlessness to instead a place of empowerment. Don't give away your sparkle. Instead, create a life that lifts you up so you get to lead your life from joy, happiness, and worthiness. This state allows you to share your sparkle and illuminate beautiful light without fear of losing your way or yourself.

Today's oil is clove - the oil of boundaries. °

Some people are going to reject you simply because you shine too brightly for them. That's OK, keep shining!

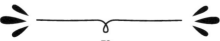

Write a list of your friends, family, colleagues or any other people in your life that life you up:

Write a list of the qualities you would love to see in those that you surround yourself with:

Now I want you to have a think about the people in your life that drain you of your sparkle or take up your time. Recognize the energy zappers around you. The ones that complain about life constantly and always need your help but ultimately do nothing to change their situation. We all have them and we can't always remove them completely. However, we can limit their impact on our lives and the time we share with them. Take a moment to note who these people are and what you can do to change things for you.

I know, I have already asked a lot of you because boundaries and relationships are tough to work through. However, if you are going to be surrounded by new energy, then you have to go and find it.

I want you to make a conscious effort to join a new group, club or activity during these next 30 days in order to meet new people because you are going to grow and manifest your own tribe. You deserve to be nourished by like-minded souls. Some people may leave your life to make space for those who should be there. Trust the process. I promise you it will be worth it.

Remember, there will be people in your life that do not want you to change or better how you feel about yourself because you serve a purpose to them. There will be people that don't want you to change. You might also, in this exercise, realize the people that take up so much of your energy and time.

Tip: I love diffusing clove with cinnamon, lime and a little dash of tea tree for a super duper boundary blend.

Take a moment to brainstorm some ideas.

DAY EIGHTEEN
FEED YOUR BODY

OK, so this might seem a little obvious, but feeding our body the right way makes us feel better inside and out. When we drink lots of water, supplement and eat a healthy plant-filled diet, then the glow on the inside shows on the outside.

Eat glitter for breakfast and shine all day.

So no more skipping breakfast or missing meals or snacking all day long on the wrong foods. We humans, especially us ladies, are emotional eaters. It's a vicious circle. We feel bad about ourselves, so we eat crap, then we talk crap to ourselves, then we go back to eating crap. Processed foods and sugar effect our mood and blood sugar, and make us gain weight. When we start to love ourselves, then we start to appreciate this vehicle—the body—that houses our amazing spirit.

Today start your day with an amazing smoothie jam packed with fresh ingredients and nutrient dense brain food to keep you shining all day long.

Today's oil is grapefruit –
the oil of honouring the body.

Beauty is being the best possible version of yourself on the inside and out. —Audrey Hepburn.

Dare to Sparkle Smoothie

Organic kale
Organic spinach
1 banana
1 cup of non-dairy milk (I like unsweetened almond)
2 cups of frozen berries
1 tablespoon of nut butter
1 tablespoon of chia seeds
1 drop of ginger essential oil (dōTERRA)
1 drop of lemon essential oil (dōTERRA)
Add water to get the desired consistency

The next part is very important. Most of us do not drink enough water daily for our body's needs. Today try drinking 8 glasses of water today. Most of us do not drink enough plain water without the frills. Yet our body needs it to thrive and survive.

Often we mistake being thirsty for hunger. So today make this your priority. Cross them off as drink them. Feel good about treating your body well. I love adding a drop of lemon or grapefruit essential oil to a big glass of water. It's good for your body and it tastes great!

Tip: Diffuse grapefruit oil to feel uplifted.

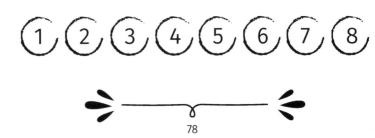

DAY NINETEEN
SHUT UP!!

Sorry to be blunt, but sometimes we just need to tell ourselves to shut up! We are constantly judging ourselves and others. If you don't believe me just try watching your brain, even for 10 minutes! Although we are much harder on ourselves than others, we do judge others as a way to feel better about ourselves. Even if it's that 'Miss Prefect's' hair is not so perfect today, so now I don't feel bad about my just got out of bed look. Am I right?

The other way of judging people is to put them on a pedestal and idolize them. It might look a little different, but it's still judging. It's also a chance for jealousy or the not good enough vibe to raise its ugly head.

In a society that profits from your self-doubt, liking yourself is a rebellious act and I'm daring you to make a start.

Why do we doubt our awesomeness? We don't even give ourselves a chance to succeed and shine. Often we have already told ourselves we can't do it, or we aren't good enough before we have even tried.

Today's oil is lemongrass - the oil of cleansing.

Change your thoughts and you will change your world. —Norman Vincent Peale.

So today's mantra is:

I am good enough and then some.

Don't let your doubts sabotage your actions. Take jealousy, for example. Often we feel jealous when someone has something we'd like. By judging and not being happy for that person, we are actually saying we aren't worthy of the same joy, success, or achievement ourselves. You are deserving though, so act like it! Whether it's a promotion, a holiday, a car, a bigger salary, or just loving yourself with confidence. Start with being happy for those that are already there. We can't know their journey to get there or where they started from. We can only work with ourselves and our journey.

Your task today is to watch the mind stuff. When you notice an ugly thought towards yourself or someone else entering your mind.

STOP. BREATHE. LET GO.

Letting go is fantastic, but what is even better is to turn these thoughts around! When you find yourself, thinking of these things be the witness. Don't beat yourself up for what your mind did. It just needs retraining and that takes learning to recognize what your habits are. So if you find yourself with negative mind chatter, acknowledge it and then add something positive to that story. With practice, you will just begin to see the beauty in others, in situations and yes... in yourself!

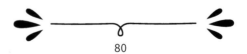

'm leaving you some space here for you to jot down any negative thoughts that you have faced today about ourself. What negative narration did you have to deal vith. Try to add some positive counter statements to the omments you add.

ip: I always feel like lemongrass essential oil blows away the negative cobwebs. It's a very invigorating oil, o I like to place a drop in the palm of my hands, rub my palms together and inhale deeply 4 or 5 times. Try diffus-ng it with cypress to clear the pathway for change.

Vhat thoughts popped up today?

How did you turn them around?

DAY TWENTY
GET OUTSIDE

There is something so magical about getting outdoors and into nature for me. Maybe it is the vastness that makes us and our problems look so small or maybe it's the beauty and all the secrets it holds. Science is proving what we've always known intuitively: nature does good things to the human brain—it makes us healthier, happier, and smarter.

When it rains look for rainbows.
When it's dark look for stars.
–Oscar Wilde.

You don't have to go on a massive hike unless you want to. You can start small and just head out for a 20-minute walk. If you don't have time for a walk, then see the grounding exercise on the next page. Try to head to nature, the woods, the ocean, the desert and away from houses, people and busyness.

Today's oil is eucalyptus - the oil of wellness. °

Do one thing each day that makes you smile.

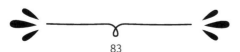

Once you get outside:

I want you to focus on your breath and notice your breathing for the next few minutes. Take some nice deep breathes and even use your exhale to take a few sighs. Stop for a moment and notice the colours, sounds and beauty surrounding you.

Feel the softness of the earth under your feet, the wind in your hair, the sun on your skin. Tap into your senses and whisper to yourself that the beauty around you is the same beauty that is within you.

Tip: Eucalyptus is a great oil for opening the airways, so take some deep breaths of it before you walk. Even better, add a drop to fractionated coconut oil and apply it to your chest area.

Grounding exercise:

Go outside for a few minutes and just stand still. Close your eyes and begin to feel the floor beneath your feet. Connect to that sensation of support and grounding. Listen carefully to your surroundings and note what you hear. Take a moment to really hear. Now move onto what do you feel? Perhaps the wind, the sun, maybe you notice if you are warm or cold. Take a moment to feel.

Open your eyes and now note what you see. Breathe in and out and notice the smells. Stand here for a few more moments and sense an all over peace. This is a great technique if you are feeling overwhelmed, stressed, anxious, or worried.

How did you feel before your walk?

How did you feel after your walk?

If you did a grounding technique, how was it?

DAY TWENTY-ONE
DANCE LIKE NO-ONE IS WATCHING

Music is the wave that carries us away from our woes. Have you noticed that? I'm sure you have. Your favourite track comes on in the most random place, your car, the supermarket, a hotel lobby, and you are transported back through your memories to another realm. In a split second, stress and worries can just vanish as if they were never there. A bad mood can be turned on its head with just the right musical intro.

So today is the day I am asking you to crank up the tunes and dance like you just don't care. Like no-one is watching and you don't have a worry in the world.

Close the curtains and shut out the world if you need to. Next I want you to find a song—your song—today's song and just boogie! Dance for the whole track. More than once if you feel called to it or even a few songs. You might really find your groove and then let it flow.

Today's oil is lime – the oil of zest for life. °

The body is a mirror of the mind, so shifting your body into a confident state can have surprising results.

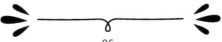

To be beautiful means to be yourself. You don't need to be accepted by others. You just need to accept yourself. —Thich Nhat Hanh.

What did you dance to?

- -

How did you feel before?

- -

- -

- -

- -

How did you feel after?

- -

- -

- -

- -

Tip: Citrus oils are our happiness in a bottle oils. Lime is uplifting but also energizing too. Try setting your space up before your dance session. Add 6 to 7 drops of lime to your diffuser and get ready to let loose with those moves.

Try this for the next week every day! List all of the songs you use and how you feel:

Song or Artist   Feelings

- - - - - - - - - - - - - - - -   - - - - - - - - - - - - - - - -

- - - - - - - - - - - - - - - -   - - - - - - - - - - - - - - - -

- - - - - - - - - - - - - - - -   - - - - - - - - - - - - - - - -

- - - - - - - - - - - - - - - -   - - - - - - - - - - - - - - - -

- - - - - - - - - - - - - - - -   - - - - - - - - - - - - - - - -

- - - - - - - - - - - - - - - -   - - - - - - - - - - - - - - - -

- - - - - - - - - - - - - - - -   - - - - - - - - - - - - - - - -

- - - - - - - - - - - - - - - -   - - - - - - - - - - - - - - - -

- - - - - - - - - - - - - - - -   - - - - - - - - - - - - - - - -

- - - - - - - - - - - - - - - -   - - - - - - - - - - - - - - - -

- - - - - - - - - - - - - - - -   - - - - - - - - - - - - - - - -

- - - - - - - - - - - - - - - -   - - - - - - - - - - - - - - - -

- - - - - - - - - - - - - - - -   - - - - - - - - - - - - - - - -

- - - - - - - - - - - - - - - -   - - - - - - - - - - - - - - - -

- - - - - - - - - - - - - - - -   - - - - - - - - - - - - - - - -

DAY TWENTY-TWO
YOUR AWESOME LIST

You are awesome if you hadn't figured that out yet! And this is kind of the goal and purpose of this book. It's about integrating self-care and self-love tools to uncover our awesomeness. It has been there the whole time, I can assure you. For some reason, we become a little blind to it.

Now is the time to make sure YOU know it like I know it. You are going to write a list. Not just any list. It's an awesome list.

Do not dull your beautiful light to make someone else feel more comfortable. Be who you are without hesitation and you will inspire others to shine too. —Anna Taylor.

On your list, you are going to put all your achievements to date and you get to choose which ones. Maybe becoming a mum, or getting a great job, or looking after others or learning to drive, graduating somewhere, travelling, embracing a passion, facing a fear. You choose!

Today's oil is roman chamomile – the oil of spiritual purpose.

Shine like the whole universe is yours.

What experiences have you had, that you can look back on and feel pride for. If you are struggling with this task today, ask someone who knows you well to give you a hand. Sometimes we aren't able to see the achievements we have gained for what they are but others can.

Tip: Try diffusing roman chamomile with lavender or ylang ylang to create a nurturing space for truth, playfulness, and purpose.

Fill them in below:

Yep I want to see more.

Pretty awesome list right! A great place to visit when your sparkle is dimming a little and self-doubt is creeping in because you have forgotten just how amazing you are.

DAY TWENTY-THREE
STOP COMPARING YOURSELF TO OTHERS

Why do we do that? Look at others and compare ourselves? This is a lose-lose situation. When we compare ourselves, it puts us in a negative spin. It tells the universe that we believe that we don't deserve to have what others have. It causes us to judge ourselves and often decide we are 'not enough' as we are right now.

It is often while travelling through the dark that you find the ones who shine the brightest in your life. For they are the ones who remind you of your own beautiful light and show up without a second thought, in your pain and well as your glory.
—Anna Taylor.

Rarely do we look at those less fortunate than ourselves and think about the blessings of our life. Although sometimes we judge others and their appearance or behaviour as a way to feel better about ourselves as if we are superior and therefore not as bad or lowly as we first imagined we were. This really isn't any better.

Today's oil is bergamot - the oil of self acceptance.

It's never too late to be what you might have been.
—George Elliot.

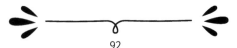

92

Life is not a competition. We don't see the whole story for any other person, therefore comparisons are unfair. We are all living a different adventure. You are one of a kind, so how can anyone be compared to you or you to them.

So how do we start? We start by being happy for those who are happy and for those who have the things we dream to have, a family, career, a new car, or a healthy body.

Instead of comparing yourself to others, take time to reflect on your own journey. Look back to where you were a year ago or 5 or 10 years ago. How has life changed and improved. Look at your own successes and achievements. Focus on you and your journey.

So the next time you start to compare yourself or your life to others—STOP! And follow below.

1 Gain awareness—most often we don't realize we are doing this.

2 Count your blessings.

3 Focus on your strengths.

4 Be OK with imperfection.

5 Don't knock others down.

6 Focus on the journey.

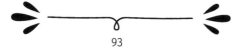

7   Learn to love yourself and know you are enough.

8   Use others as inspiration to spur you on to show the
    world what you have to offer.

The day she let go of the things that were
weighting her down was the day she began to
shine the brightest. —Katrina Mayer.

For the next week I want you to gain an awareness of the
areas in your life that comparing and judging happens.
Write them down. Once we have an awareness of where
we are feeling difficulties, we can focus on making the
shift in our consciousness.

Each of us shines in a different way but this
doesn't make our light less bright.

DAY TWENTY-FOUR
CLUTTER BE GONE

We surround ourselves with stuff. To be honest, we often lose ourselves or even hide ourselves with stuff. My yoga teacher once said 'tidy house, tidy mind' and I know this to be true for me. Stuff weighs us down physically, emotionally, and energetically.

Think about the dilemmas we encounter because of stuff. Things that we have bought and no longer love but can't part with because they cost so much. Perhaps you were gifted an item or left something by someone who has passed, that you loved. You don't love the item but you love the person and so you often keep it because you feel immense guilt for wanting to let it go. Like you are somehow letting that person down.

Honor your body-celebrate it. Thank it for all it does.

So what I am asking you to do is start a mini revolution in your closet and if you are feeling really brave then your bedroom too and eventually it might encompass your home.

Today's oil is wile orange – the oil of abundance and inner child playfulness.

Life's a balance of holding on and letting go.

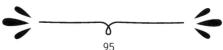

This might fill some of you with dread and horror, so we can start slowly. How many of us keep an outfit or item of clothing because it cost a lot or once upon a time we could fit into it. These items are holding energetic space ladies! If it doesn't make your heart smile when you hold it or put it on, then let it go. You are making space for items that should be in your life.

Getting to a place where we have a select few treasured items we just love to wear and that make us feel amazing is where we are headed.

The point is to be a realist, though, when separating the stuff you keep from the stuff you don't. Ask yourself what you really use, what you love, and what you need, both now and in the future. We change and so do our bodies. Today we are embracing how we look now and how we want to look in clothes as we are not holding onto the past.

I actually look forward to doing this a few times a year. Put aside the whole evening to play 'dress up' just as we did as kids. I get everything out of the closets and the drawers and I mean everything. Nothing lurking in the corners is left.

Add to this a glass of wine, some uplifting music, and a yummy oil in my diffuser and off I go. There is a 'keep' pile, this contains the clothes I love right now at this moment. There is a 'go' pile and that gets bagged up to go to the charity shop. Finally, there is the 'I'll think about it' pile.

This pile sits out on the side for a week or so as I get a handle on how I feel about those items. Am I drawn to wearing them? Would I miss them?

If doing your whole wardrobe all at once is too much, you can start smaller, but I don't believe in doing things by half measures. We have one life and I for one want to be living it to the max and finding joy in every day.

Once you have a bag of things you don't want anymore, then either donate them, recycle or perhaps have a clothing swap with your friends and make a celebration of it. Just don't be tempted to keep them 'just in case' because they still hold that stagnant energy.

I have to say I love clothing swaps because it's a way for the things that don't serve you anymore to find a happy home with your friends. I also know that for some people, the charity shop is a clean break. It's gone to be loved from afar and where you aren't reminded of parting with it.

Now you have made space in your life for the 'new you', you also get to start planning! What new or new to you (thrift shopping is my favourite) item are you going to get now to replace the things you let go of? Go on and treat yourself. If you don't usually put yourself first it is time to change that. Fill your own cup!

List some treasures you'd like to find for yourself:
(PS you deserve it)

List some of the things you let go of:
(PS feel really proud here)

- -

- -

- -

- -

- -

- -

- -

- -

- -

- -

- -

- -

- -

- -

- -

DAY TWENTY-FIVE
SHARE YOUR SMILE

Be brave. Be bold. Be you! Today I'm asking you to share that beautiful smile of yours. Share it with your friends, your family, social media and of course the best part... yep total strangers.

Let your smile change the world, but don't let the world change your smile. —Connor Franta.

The power of a smile shows you just how brightly you shine for everyone else even if you don't see it in yourself yet. Still not convinced? A smile shows someone that you are happy, joyful, accepted in yourself and all those things make you utterly adorable and contagious. When we offer out a smile to the world, we have the power to turn someone's day around if they are the recipient of that beaming smile. It makes the person receiving the smile feel wanted, seen, and accepted. Who knows how many people that person will smile at because you gifted them yours. Smiling is all about connecting to other beautiful beings.

Today's oil is cheer blend - the oil of enjoyment.

Keep shining beautiful one,
the world need your light.

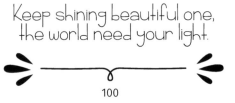

(Try and keep a tally today and fill in the questions below)

Share your experiences of today:

How many people did you smile at?

Did anything unexpected happen?

How many people smiled back at you?

How did you feel before, during and after?

Tip: When I have to go out and be less introverted I love to put my happy citrus oils like cheer in my diffuser necklace so that you can smell those happy vibes all day long.

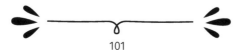

DAY TWENTY-SIX
LISTS OF JOY

What brings you happiness? What things, light you up inside? What brings you joy, smiles, and laughter? Think of the moments where you literally feel on top of the world. Those are the things you need to fill your life with every single day. I can't believe how many times I hear women say that they don't have the chance to do the things that nurture them because they are too busy. Seriously, what is more important than your own physical and mental health. When did we begin to think we don't deserve as much time and love as we want. We often put our happiness last, yet we can't fill the cup of others if we don't fill up our own first. It's time to start with you. It doesn't need to be an all or nothing situation. You do, however, need to be in control of the only person you can be in control of and that is YOU.

If you don't know where you are going, at least enjoy where you are at.

Your task today is to write your joy list on the next page.

Today's oil is tangerine - the oil of spontaneity.

Your soul is made of stars.

It can be big joys or small ones. This is all about you. Once you have written your list, I want you to do at least one thing you have written. You got this! Create your happy every day because you deserve the best.

1 _ _ _ _ _ _ _ _ _ _ _ _ _ _ _   11 _ _ _ _ _ _ _ _ _ _ _ _ _ _ _

2 _ _ _ _ _ _ _ _ _ _ _ _ _ _ _   12 _ _ _ _ _ _ _ _ _ _ _ _ _ _ _

3 _ _ _ _ _ _ _ _ _ _ _ _ _ _ _   13 _ _ _ _ _ _ _ _ _ _ _ _ _ _ _

4 _ _ _ _ _ _ _ _ _ _ _ _ _ _ _   14 _ _ _ _ _ _ _ _ _ _ _ _ _ _ _

5 _ _ _ _ _ _ _ _ _ _ _ _ _ _ _   15 _ _ _ _ _ _ _ _ _ _ _ _ _ _ _

6 _ _ _ _ _ _ _ _ _ _ _ _ _ _ _   16 _ _ _ _ _ _ _ _ _ _ _ _ _ _ _

7 _ _ _ _ _ _ _ _ _ _ _ _ _ _ _   17 _ _ _ _ _ _ _ _ _ _ _ _ _ _ _

8 _ _ _ _ _ _ _ _ _ _ _ _ _ _ _   18 _ _ _ _ _ _ _ _ _ _ _ _ _ _ _

9 _ _ _ _ _ _ _ _ _ _ _ _ _ _ _   19 _ _ _ _ _ _ _ _ _ _ _ _ _ _ _

10 _ _ _ _ _ _ _ _ _ _ _ _ _ _ _   20 _ _ _ _ _ _ _ _ _ _ _ _ _ _ _

Tip: Add a little spearmint to your tangerine to create a refreshing and uplifting blend.

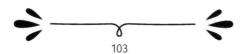

DAY TWENTY-SEVEN
GRAB A HUG

Doesn't a good hug feel absolutely amazing! They can feel wishy-washy too when people pretend at them. What I mean by that is when you go in for a hug and you are expecting a warm embrace and instead you get a shoulder bump and a limp pat on the back. I know you have experienced what I have fondly termed, a wet lettuce hug at some point. The awkward kind of hug that ends up not being a hug at all.

It's the real soul lifting hugs that I am talking about. I have been an advocate for hugging for a number of years. Research has shown that hugs are extremely effective at healing sickness, disease, loneliness, depression, anxiety, and stress. A good hug should last a good 5 to 10 seconds with hearts pressed. This can help our mood and lift our emotions, make us feel self-worth and self-esteem. It can physically help our bodies by relaxing our muscles, boosting our immune system as well as balancing your nervous system.

There is a saying by Virginia Satir, a respected family therapist, "We need four hugs a day for survival. We need eight hugs a day for maintenance. We need twelve hugs a day for growth."

Today's oil is ginger - the oil of empowerment.°
Be yourself and never apologize for it.

Today your goal is to get as many good real squeezy hugs as you can muster. The hugs can be with family, friends or even strangers. I want you to be brave and try for at least one hug with a stranger.

How many hugs did you get?

How did you feel before, during and after?

What was the response of the person you hugged?

Tip: I like to diffuse ginger with lemon and bergamot for focus, self acceptance and empowerment.

DAY TWENTY-EIGHT
MIRROR MIRROR

Mirror mirror on the wall who's the fairest of them all?

You did not wake up today to be mediocre.

Why is it that so many of us have a hard time looking in the mirror and saying 'I Love You!' The simple answer is that we haven't yet figured out how amazing we are. We are still on the trail of... if I was thinner, or my nose was different or my hair... I could go on all day. We live in a society that spreads perfection all over social media. It simply doesn't exist and if we can't find the love and happiness within ourselves, then even if we drop the twenty pounds, or get a nose job or whatever it might be, we still will not be happy.

So today is day one of the rest of your life. You may feel silly talking to yourself in the mirror. You may feel awkward saying I love you.

Today's oil is lemon –
the oil of focus and rationality.

It's never too late to be what you might have been. —George Elliot.

You will get a sense of how your relationship really is with yourself. Start slow if you need with an—"I like you!" If saying "I love you," is too tough. Don't put your mask on first either—your makeup. I want you to try this straight out of bed in the morning and in your natural beautiful state. You can do it throughout the day too as it gets easier. I get quite hilarious with mine.... I've been known to wink at myself... point at my reflection and say "How you doing?" In a funny voice! Mainly because after years of practice I actually like the person I see staring back at me and she is my best friend.

Maybe you found that you focused in on the parts of 'you' that you don't like. Don't judge yourself. Remember old habits take a while to break. We need to create new habits to override the old ones. I have left space for you to keep adding to this experience so that with time you can see the changes that happen. This is a life-long practice that has to start somewhere and today is the day.

Day one of Mirror Mirror:

How did you feel?

- -

- -

What was the most challenging part?

- -

- -

What parts of you do you find hard to love?

- -

- -

Which parts of you are easier to love?

- -

- -

Six months later:

How did you feel?

What was the most challenging part?

What parts of you do you find hard to love?

Which parts of you are easier to love?

One year later:

How did you feel?

What was the most challenging part?

What parts of you do you find hard to love?

Which parts of you are easier to love?

DAY TWENTY-NINE
SECRET KINDNESS

I love random acts of kindness. I mean who doesn't like feeling like you have made someone else's day better. I like the fact that the simple act of doing and giving gives our hearts joy and purpose. To be honest, when I do these things for others, I think I receive more than I am even given because of the experience.

Most of us don't do things intentionally to get thank yous from others, but there are often expectations. How many times have you done something and expected a result? And then, what's even worse, it wasn't the response you expected? Disappointment is a tough pill to swallow. So this way of doing things helps us focus on the most important part of this which is the giving.

When you learn to write your own story, the possibilities are endless.

Let's get creative and have fun making life better for those around us. We are becoming such a cold and disconnected planet, so let's spread the love and the joy every day.

Today's oil is elevation - the oil of joy and happiness.

Don't dream your life, live your dreams.

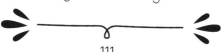

Write down some ideas of things that you could do to make others around you feel loved. Try to do at least one today. Note that the emphasis is on 'Secret Kindness' so you can't actively let them know it is you. Remember it's not about the "thank you," it's about the deed itself. It's about gaining pleasure in being of service and offering kindness to someone else.

Some ideas for you that I have tried were leaving flowers, chocolates, notes, or gifts for people. Paying for the people behind me in Starbucks. Emailing someone's boss to say what an amazing job they are doing. Now it's your turn to brainstorm a few ideas.

How did you do? Write about what you chose to do for someone else today.

How did it make you feel?

Would you do anything differently next time?

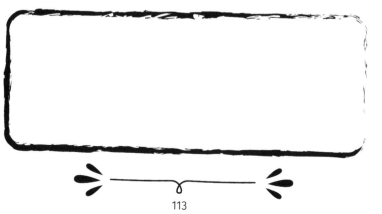

DAY THIRTY
CREATE YOUR HAPPY

Isn't it funny how we look at our lives. Doing things that make us happy often feels like a guilty pleasure that we don't deserve. Why is it that we put everyone else first?

Love your whole story even if it hasn't been the perfect fairytale.

We are living in a world where we are not enough, where we feel the need to please everyone and where there is never enough time. Fortunately, there is more than enough time, but we need to learn to let go of these high standards that we have set for ourselves. We don't need to be everything to everyone. Succeeding in life has been painted to us as being busy, never failing, and working hard. Where has all the joy, fun and play in life vanished to.

Today you are going to write a list of things that make you 'enough' and then choose right now to go share that with someone you know and encourage them to do the same. You deserve to be happy every single day and so do they.

Today's oil is melissa - the oil of soul purpose.

Don't dream your life, live your dreams.

We create our own universe, and so we are the only ones that can make this happen. Happiness is inherently our natural state, so learn to find what makes you sparkle.

Write keywords or elaborate on what makes you more than enough in this world. How would other people describe you? Toot your own horn and do it with enthusiasm.

Tip: Try diffusing with citrus bliss or putting on the pulse points and your heart.

DAY THIRTY PLUS ONE
JOURNAL IT

When I first started to put these tools together, I had imagined that 30 days was enough but who was I kidding! We all know that these 30 days are just an intro to the rest of our lives as we seek to find our magic again. Finding love for ourselves so that we can truly love others from a place of wholeness. We had it as children. We saw the magic in everything including ourselves. Then we allowed others to cast doubt in our minds.

Magic is believing in yourself, if you can, that you can make anything happen.
—Johann Wolfgang von Goethe.

So I have added this extra day in for you to get creative and inspired. Journaling is whatever you want it to be. The key is to do is consistently and regularly. You might want to write your thoughts or gratitudes, or quotes that have inspired you or a combination of all of these.

Put your journal somewhere that you will see it and use it every single day even if you just write one word. Everything starts with effort. You got this! Time to invest in yourself every darn day!

Today's oil is your choice - what uplifts and inspires you? What oil adds a pep to your step? Choose that one.
xoxo

BIBLIOGRAPHY

love this book so much and I recommend it to everyone
can. Seriously you should buy it! The emotional use of
essential oils is the part about oils that fascinates me
the most and this book is my holy grail.

Essential Emotions — Your Guide to Process, Release and
Live Free - 8th Edition.

Passages marked with ◊ are from Essential Emotions.

ABOUT THE AUTHOR

Lou Meggiato is a creative and passionate soul, who has found her path in life. She works with her clients as a Registered Aromatherapist, Yoga Teacher, Women's Life Coach, and a sparkly designer.

She has spent years creating tools to support women to shine. She also holds women's retreats to help us take time back for ourselves while experiencing nurturing and self-love. Lou enjoys collaborating with other beautiful souls on her 'goddess' retreats to bring their gifts to the world and her clients.

'Dare to Sparkle' is her debut book and is an easy to access journey into finding time and love for yourself. Lou grew up in the UK with her brother and parents. Her parents taught her to believe in herself and that she could achieve anything she set her mind to. She moved to Canada in 2007 and has called British Columbia home ever since.

Lou can be contacted for one-on-one work or to see her events and other offerings, visit:

www.mandalaessentials.com

Made in the USA
Coppell, TX
05 November 2020

40820743R00066